Discover The True You

Buster Books

Contents

About This Book

It's time to get to grips with the true you! With the help of funky quizzes and some serious self-analysis you'll discover exactly who you are, and what makes you tick.

No stone will be left unturned in your voyage of self-discovery. Are you ready to find out what people really think about you? Do you consider yourself an eco-warrior, determined to save the planet, or do you still need to learn what it means to be green? You'll learn everything about yourself, from who you are to your natural style. You'll find out how a simple doodle can reveal your feelings, and how dreams can reflect what is going on in your life.

Investigate your boy karma and discover whether you're going to be lucky in love. Is your current crush a mate or a date? Then there's your love destiny — what's written in the stars? A career quiz will even help you think about jobs most suited to your personality.

Pass this book around your friends and find out what they are made of. So, what are you waiting for? Pick up your pen and discover the true you.

All About You

Everyone knows how important it is to be yourself, but how well do you really know the true you? Have you ever wondered how others see you? Do people ever tell you that you are bossy? Do you take the time to do your bit for the planet? Would you consider yourself open to new opinions and experiences? Now is the time to find all of this out. Complete these personal quizzes and begin the exploration of the true you.

How Assertive Are You?

OK – which of these categories describes you best – shy and mild-mannered or extroverted and bossy? Will you stop at nothing when it comes to getting your own way, or are you a chilled, laid-back, live-and-let-live kind of girl? Find out with this fun quiz.

1. You and your friend are deciding what to wear to a school disco. You notice that she has a cool new skirt which you'd love to borrow, but she isn't keen on the idea. Do you...

A. ...refuse to go if she doesn't let you wear the skirt? You're not used to being told you can't have something.

B. ...admit defeat, but search frantically for another (cooler) one to wear? Hers may be great, but you refuse to be outshone on the dance floor.

C. ...burst into tears and cry for so long that you miss the start of the disco.

2. You're directing a play in drama class with a group of friends. Your rehearsals are...

A.   ...a complete disaster. No one knows their lines and they're all messing about. In fact, your teacher has to step in to take control.

B.   ...full on! Everyone knows who's in charge and works hard under your command.

C.   ...chilled, but you're getting results. Your relaxed style has got everyone cooperating to make this play perfect.

3. You and your little brother are sent out to pick up some groceries. You don't want to take him along but your mum insists. Do you...

A.   ...refuse to put up with any nonsense and snap at him constantly? You can't believe you're being forced to cart him around like this.

B.   ...grit your teeth and hope none of your friends spot you? You'd never live it down if you were seen.

C.   ...give in to his pleas for chocolate and buy him five bars? Anything to keep him quiet.

4. You and your classmates are on the school playing field for a game of rounders. Who gets to pick teams?

A.   Being captain sounds cool, but you're far too nervous to put yourself forward. Your face turns red just thinking about it.

B.   Everyone wants the chance, so you put together a rota that allows a different person to pick each week.

C.   You do, of course. You've been captain so many times no one bothers to argue with you anymore.

5. Your best mate has made a really bad decision that affects you, but she doesn't seem to realize it. How do you react?

A.   Take her aside and calmly explain exactly how the decision has affected you, and the problems it has caused. If she's a real mate she'll understand.

B.   Keep quiet. She's your best friend and you wouldn't want to upset her.

C.   React quickly and loudly and stay up all night making a list of reasons why she's wrong.

6. A surprise birthday party has been thrown for you, and you are called to make a speech. You can't possibly refuse. Do you...

A. ...stand up proudly and launch into a glorious monologue that Shakespeare would have been proud to have written?

B. ...take the floor, but feel so embarrassed and self-conscious that your few words are barely audible? You can't bear all that attention on you, even if they are your friends.

C. ...decide to make the best of it by simply thanking everyone for coming, and sit back down. There's no need to overdo it.

7. You and your mates are coming home after seeing the latest film. As you are walking home together, the lady next door puts her head over the wall and yells at you to be quiet. Do you...

A. ...apologize to her face, but giggle about her as soon as you're home?

B. ...refuse to admit you were making that much noise and talk back to her until she threatens to tell your mum?

C. ...rush into your house? You are so embarrassed, you'll think twice about ever having your friends around again.

8. You're late for your first day of summer work when a charity worker approaches you on the street, collecting money. He tries to engage you in conversation. Do you...

A. ...sail right on past without even acknowledging him? Now is not a good time to be bothering you.

B. ...feel obliged to stop and chat? Visions of being sacked run through your mind, but he asked so nicely you just couldn't refuse.

C. ...explain the situation to the guy, and give your apologies, but carry on your way? It wouldn't do to be late on your first day.

9. One Saturday in the park, you spot a girl who has just moved to your area. You'd like to get to know her, but she's with a boy. Do you...

A. ...assume they're going out and not bother? They probably wouldn't want you cramping their style.

B. ...run over and invite them to your house for an evening of videos and junk food? They'd be mad to say no.

C. ...decide not to pester them now? You'll go around to her house later to introduce yourself.

10. You and your friends have got tickets to see your fave boy band. You really want to meet the group after the concert, but the crowd is huge. Drastic action is needed. Do you...

A. ...tell one of your mates to fake a fainting fit and insist that the security man carries her backstage to recover? Result!

B. ...try to push to the front, but, finding there are just too many people, give up and go home? Maybe next time you'll be lucky.

C. ...get to the front no matter what? You squeeze through the crush at a snail's pace and some people give you nasty looks, but you don't care.

Now turn to page 78 and work out your score.

Keen On Green?

When it comes to the environment, are you an avid defender of the Earth, or a poor excuse for an eco-warrior? Would you rather hit the shops than hug a tree? Perhaps you're an expert on all things green? Try this quiz to find out!

> **1.** Your school is organizing a trip to a rainforest and you've been voted onto the fund-raising committee. Your first decision is to...

A. ...quit! You've no intention of spending any more time at school than you have to, even if there is a holiday at the end of it.

B. ...organize a campaign to get people interested in the trip by telling them how rainforests are being destroyed. It's important that everyone knows why you're going, and what's at stake.

C. ...have a meeting to discuss how to raise money. You're not really sure about all the issues, but you might as well join in and learn as you go.

14

2. It's up to you to choose a fab holiday destination for your family. Do you go for...

A. ...camping in the Lake District? You can't wait to enjoy the great outdoors and get back to nature.

B. ...Disneyland, where you can enjoy yourself in comfort and everything is done for you?

C. ...a remote tropical beach where you can spend hours noting down all the different butterflies you spot?

3. You see a photo of a supermodel in a magazine wearing a fur coat. How do you feel?

A. Sick! You can't believe an animal died for fashion. If you were the model you'd refuse to wear it.

B. A bit sad, but there's nothing you can do about it. It wouldn't stop you buying the mag again though.

C. You hadn't even noticed it was fur. You're really interested in fashion, so as long as it looks good it doesn't matter.

4. How often do you eat organic food?

A. You've never heard of it and you don't do the shopping, so you couldn't say.

B. All the time. You know it's organic because your parents grow it in the back garden.

C. You've noticed it in the supermarket, but you're not sure if mum buys any. You might mention it as it's supposed to be good for you and for the environment.

5. Little things can make such a big difference. How green are you around the house?

A. Amazingly green! You were born to save the planet and are always switching off lights, tending your vegetable patch and bugging your parents to get recycling.

B. You don't even know what being green means. All that fuss about the environment is dull. You often leave the house without turning off the TV.

C. You feel you do your bit and you're cool with that. If everyone did a little to help it would make a big difference.

6. A new road is being built right through the middle of a park where you like to hang out. Do you...

A. ...get your friends together and write a letter to the council? If that doesn't work you'll start a petition. It's a really nice place to go and chill out and it'd be terrible to lose it.

B. ...spend hours in the park making notes on the plants and animals it is home to? You'll tell the council as soon as possible and make them see what their plans could do to local wildlife.

C. ...moan to your friends but do nothing? Come to think of it, the new road will make it easier to get to the shops on Saturdays.

7. Your older brother is taking you with him to buy his first car. However, the one he's keen on only takes leaded petrol. Do you...

A. ...fail to even notice? This car is sooo cool you're already begging him to try it out. He'll be able to drive you around now instead of your parents!

B. ...ask the sales person to suggest cars that are greener. You've studied catalytic converters at school and with your impressive knowledge you point out all the negative aspects of leaded petrol.

C. ...throw a strop and tell him what an evil person he is for even thinking about polluting the earth further. He should stick to public transport — there are far too many cars on the road anyway.

8. A company planning to build a huge new shopping complex is chopping down a wood near your home, but eco-warriors have started living in the trees and are refusing to come down. What do you think?

A. Cool! You can't wait to grab your rope, hot drinks flask and torch, and join the nature-loving hippies. It's for the trees, Man!

B. They're creating a scene for nothing. This shopping complex is going to bring in lots of cash and provide jobs for people. How can anyone have a problem with more shops?

C. You can see their point, but you don't think they'll be able to stop the diggers in the end. However, you take them supplies in the meantime.

9. Your best friend has just come back from a family holiday in Thailand laden with pressies. She's bought you a pretty box made out of ivory. Do you...

A. ...feel guilty because you know an elephant died to make it, but accept it anyway? It was nice of her to think of you and it is very pretty.

B. ...add it to your collection of ivory trinkets.

C. ...politely refuse to take it? You're surprised that your best friend didn't know better, and even you start to question your friendship with someone who doesn't think about protecting endangered species.

10. Your school is having an Environment Week to get everyone thinking about green issues. Are you getting involved?

A. Of course! You're organizing most of it — making posters and leaflets, and holding meetings.

B. You're taking part in a few events and you're actually enjoying learning something about the planet.

C. The week is going sooo slowly because it's not something that really interests you.

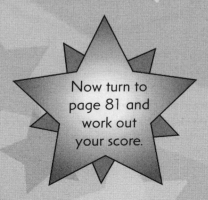

Now turn to page 81 and work out your score.

Are You Open-Minded?

Are you the epitome of tolerance and understanding, or a little more cautious in giving your approval? Do you welcome other opinions with open arms, or do you think you've got it all pretty much sussed already? This quiz will help you find out.

> **1.** A new girl, with really alternative dress sense, starts at your school. You know she's going to get noticed, and maybe not in a good way. At lunchtime, do you...

A. ...join in the gossiping about her? Well, she should try to fit in a bit better, shouldn't she?

B. ...invite her to join you? You want to know where she got her funky trousers.

C. ...give her a smile across the canteen, but go back to your fish and chips?

2. Your parents are taking you out for the evening. You fancy the movies, but they suggest the theatre. How do you react?

A. Figure it could be pretty cool to watch a play. You like having different interests and it'll make your parents happy.

B. With horror. It's obviously part of an evil plan to make you more cultured. You shouldn't have to do things you don't want to.

C. Arrange to see the movie with friends another day. You're not really into the whole drama thing, but hey, it's a free night out.

3. You are on a first date with a boy you really like. He has taken you to a swish restaurant — and has ordered you a dish of something you would never normally consider eating. What do you do?

A. You make it clear to your date that you are not really keen, but you are willing to try something new to flatter his tastes. You take a deep breath — one mouthful can't hurt.

B. Eeeew! No matter how much you want to impress your date with your sophisticated tastes, this is too much. You tell him outright that there is no way you would ever eat something like that.

C. You dig right in, no question. Nothing ventured, nothing gained, right? In fact, you discover you really like it and order seconds.

4. A boy who lives in your street asks you out on a date. He's friendly and funny, but everyone knows he has a nerdy key-ring collection. What do you do?

A. You're worried that people will call you a nerd too, so you decide to say no, thanks.

B. He may not be your usual type, but it's probably worth going on one date at least.

C. You still think he's cool to have a hobby, even if it isn't something you're interested in. This could be the start of something wonderful!

5. Your best friend wants you to go and see a new band with her, but their music is really not your scene. Do you...

A. ...go along, but suspect you'll be checking your watch every five minutes?

B. ...decide to go and enjoy it? You might even love them and end up buying a T-shirt on the way out.

C. ...tell her no way? Suggest she takes someone else who's into that kind of thing.

6. You feel like a complete change of image. Do you...

A. ...paint your nails an unusual colour?
B. ...put on an outfit you would never usually wear?
C. ...dye your hair purple?

7. You're on a school trip to Paris. How do you and your friends spend your spare time?

A. Chilling out in each other's hotel rooms. If you do venture out your French teacher can translate for you.

B. You persuade your teacher to hit the shops with you. After all, this is Paris and the clothes are to die for.

C. You visit a different attraction each day and make sure you are armed with your phrase book, so you can try talking to the people you meet.

8. Your cousin joins a computer club and starts spending lots of time with her new friends. What do you think?

A. You're not really surprised. Her side of the family was always into nerdy hobbies.

B. You telephone her immediately to ask when the next meeting is. It's about time you joined the twenty-first century.

C. You're glad there's someone close by who can help you out when your printer packs up.

9. Your granny wants you to meet her neighbours at their weekly coffee morning. Do you...

A. ...go along, but leave before they all start talking about when they were young?

B. ...turn up and enjoy mixing with different people? As the youngest there, you're the star of the show.

C. ...tell her you have an emergency appointment at the dentist?

10. You're forced to work on a school project with a girl who is your complete opposite. What do you do?

A.   Make an effort to find out what the two of you have in common. At least no one can say you didn't try.

B.   Try to complete the project in the quickest time possible, even if you spoil your grade by doing so.

C.   Beg your teacher to let you swap partners. You can't stand the thought of working with her.

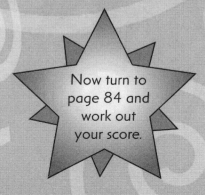

Now turn to page 84 and work out your score.

Know Your Style

This section will help you figure out your style, inside and out. With the personal style quiz you'll discover what your hobbies, your bedroom, the music you listen to and the qualities you look for in a friend say about you. Are you a die-hard party animal or a quiet, creative type? Complete the fashion chart on pages 28 to 32 and learn how much looks matter to you and what your clothes reveal about you. Then put pen to paper and amaze your friends as you become an expert on deciphering their doodles.

What Is Your Fashion Type?

Have you ever wondered if you've got your own personal style? Some people just copy the current fashion trends. Some change continously, revamping their entire wardrobe. For others, clothes are merely a necessity for warmth and modesty. Which profile fits you the best? Do you like glitter, bright colours and cutting-edge style or do you prefer a more mainstream look? Do you like to dress up to the nines or let your natural assets speak for themselves? Do this quiz and find out.

Place a tick beside the statements you agree with and make a note of the symbol beside it.

You can easily spend more than 30 minutes getting ready in the morning.	★
On a first date, it is important to dress to impress.	♥
You could easily wear head-to-toe black, 24-7.	☾
You would be so upset to discover your fave look is on every catwalk and would have to stop wearing it because it's too trendy.	★
You choose bright, colourful and fun jewellery over classic gold and silver.	♥
You usually wear your hair up or pinned to the side.	●
You much prefer a little powder and lip gloss to going all out on make-up.	☾

You prefer jeans and a cute T-shirt to skirts and heels.	🌙 (crescent moon)
You prefer pastel colours to dark colours.	❤️ (heart)
You like wearing skirts.	❤️ (heart)
You would describe yourself as happy, friendly and outgoing.	🌙 (crescent moon)
It's very important to you what others think about your style.	● (circle)
You like to use lots of sparkly accessories.	❤️ (heart)
You've got more shoes than you can keep track of.	⭐ (star)

You would never wear blue and black together.	🌙
You like to buy clothes from second-hand shops.	⬤
You own a matching hat, scarf and gloves set.	🌙
You are the proud owner of a pair of the latest fashionable trainers.	⭐
You've often thought about becoming a model.	❤️
You think fashion design would be a cool job to do.	⬤
You tend to read the fashion pages of a magazine first.	⭐

You like it if people comment on your clothes, good or bad.	●
You always feel comfortable in everything you wear.	☾
You always ensure your nails are painted to match your outfit.	♥
You absolutely love getting ready in the morning.	★
You've worn everything in your wardrobe at least once in the past year.	●
You are known to suffer from a 'closet full of clothes and nothing to wear'.	★
You absolutely love shopping for clothes.	♥

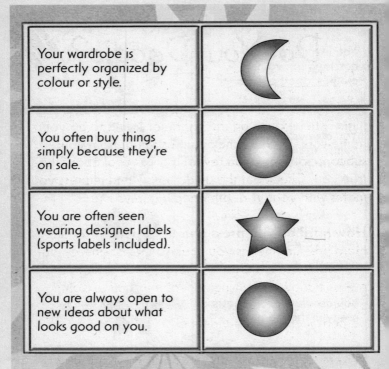

Your wardrobe is perfectly organized by colour or style.	🌙
You often buy things simply because they're on sale.	🔴
You are often seen wearing designer labels (sports labels included).	⭐
You are always open to new ideas about what looks good on you.	🔴

Which symbol have you ticked the most?

Turn to page 86 and read your profile.

Do You Doodle?

Doodles are the little drawings and scribbles that you make when you're on the phone or trying to do your homework. Because they come straight from your subconscious they can reveal a great deal about the true you. Check out the guide below and impress your mates with your in-depth doodle analysis.

How hard do you press pen to paper?
Hard pressure means you have tonnes of energy, but this could also manifest as aggression. Medium pressure shows a well-balanced personality. Light pressure means you're sensitive and thoughtful, but perhaps lacking in confidence.

Where do you position the doodle on the page?
Centre – you are outgoing and need attention, but may also occasionally require time-out from those around you.
Left – you tend to live in the past and are maybe anxious about others discovering the real you.
Top – you are enthusiastic and don't like to follow the crowd.
Bottom – you are a practical person, but are sometimes prone to feeling blue.
At the edges – you are a quiet person, who doesn't necessarily want to stand out in a crowd.

Now, what do you find yourself doodling? Read on...

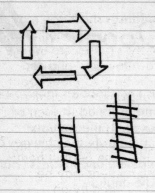

Arrows, ladders and stairs show you like working towards goals, and that you can be quite aggressive about this. If the arrows are pointing upwards then you're on the road to success; if they are going in different directions then you have many options but you can't choose between them.

Repetitive shapes like borders and waves are calming. You are careful and patient and like being in control.

Bars and lines, especially those that crisscross, show you're feeling suffocated and stressed. You may need to get out of a difficult situation.

Shading in your doodles may mean you're just bored, but you might also be feeling anxious or insecure. Have a look at what you're colouring in and then find it on the list. It might help you figure out what you're having problems with.

Buildings show you may be looking for stability and safety. Houses are usually drawn by girls, and can show how you feel about your home environment. Is the front door open or closed? Is there smoke coming from the chimney? A less than perfect home environment may be represented by an asymmetrical structure without windows.

Food doodles usually mean the scribbler is hungry – they may be on a diet.

Hearts can mean you're in love, or that you're a sentimental or romantic person. If your heart has a barrier around it then you're not in the mood for a relationship right now. Often hearts don't have anything to do with romance. The bigger they are, the more attention you need. Think of the celebrities who draw a heart with their autograph – they love to be in the spotlight.

Animals mean you want to protect and defend others.

Celestial shapes such as stars, moons and suns reveal ambition and optimism. You're a high-flyer and you want everyone to know you're going to get to the top.

Abstract drawings, such as lots of shapes next to each other, show patience, but only if parts are carefully filled in. If the shapes have thick outlines and sharp angles you are showing a lack of concentration.

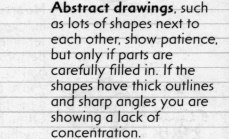

Games, such as noughts and crosses, mean you have a competitive streak.

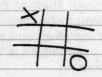

Geometric shapes, such as squares, rectangles and triangles, show a super-organized brain. You're efficient and like to plan things out.

Mazes suggest that you feel you are in a tight spot. Alternatively, it could be a sign of the need for protection from a threatening element in your life.

Question marks signify a difficult decision, or doubt about your role in life.

A **robot** is an indication that you may be unsatisfied with your life, and perhaps feel lacking in self-confidence and motivation.

Trees doodled without leaves or roots can reveal a sense of isolation or lack of strong family ties. Trees blowing in the wind may show instability in a relationship.

Faces

If the faces you draw are symmetrical and in proportion then you are happy with your appearance. If they are asymmetrical or something is missing from the face, you are still getting comfortable with who you are. Drawing attractive faces means you are friendly, optimistic and aware of other people's feelings. If your faces are ugly then you can sometimes be suspicious, moody, negative and lacking in self-confidence.

Eyes by themselves show curiosity, but repeated doodles of eyes may indicate a feeling of being watched.

Closed lips, which are drawn with strong pressure mean you're dying to kiss someone.

Open lips, which are drawn lightly, show that you're not shy about giving your opinion.

What Is Your Personal Style?

Your 'style' is about more than just what you wear. It's the music you listen to, your attitude to friends and family, and your approach to life. Are you always on the go or do you prefer to hang at home? Does having free time terrify you or liberate you? Take this quiz and begin to explore your personal style.

> **1.** You have an entire day to yourself with nothing planned. What do you do?

A. Catch up on some reading, listen to a few CDs and exercise your creative muscles by penning some poetry.

B. Plan something pronto. This is a perfect opportunity to check out a dance class, or that movie you've been dying to see.

C. Chill out with your family and enjoy some quality time together.

2. Your room says loads
about who you are.
What's in yours?

A. Photos cover the walls and there are old letters and cards everywhere. Soft toys line the shelves, and haven't you had that duvet since you were five?

B. Party invites and telephone numbers are strewn around. The room itself is so messy it could belong to ten people.

C. There are cushions and rugs in bright warm colours, the walls are covered with arty posters and maybe a framed poem or two.

3. What music do you
like to listen to when you're
alone in your room?

A. You choose tracks that put you in the mood for where you're going.

B. You usually have the radio on in the background, but you don't really notice what song is playing.

C. You pride yourself on your alternative tastes, so it's got to be something no one else has ever heard of.

4. Your dream house would be…

A. …a gorgeous city apartment right in the middle of the action.

B. …anything as long as it was close to friends and family.

C. …a barn in the countryside, which you could turn into a peaceful retreat.

5. What's your perfect holiday destination?

A. A beach in Portugal surrounded by friends. Sun, sea, sand and good company are all you need to make you happy.

B. Anywhere you can soak up a bit of culture. You love going somewhere new and enjoy living like a local.

C. A place where you can try out mountain-climbing, white-water rafting, snowboarding or a safari. You live for adventure.

6. What's your dream date?

A. Sitting under the stars and talking until the sun comes up.

B. Something different – such as bungee-jumping. If he's not up for it, then you're not interested.

C. Something to eat and a good film.

7. In the future you can see yourself...

A. ...helping other people as part of a charity, or maybe becoming a teacher or doctor. You want to do something that makes a difference.

B. ...putting your creative talents to good use as an actor, writer, artist or singer.

C. ...running your own business. You want a job that keeps you on your toes and is always exciting.

8. What quality do you look for most in a good friend?

A. Someone who understands you when no one else does. Having a compassionate compadre means you never lack emotional support.

B. Someone who's willing to try anything once. Variety is the spice of life, after all, and who wants a mate who always says 'no'?

C. Someone you can have a giggle with. Time spent together is never wasted when you both get into stitches and can't breathe for laughing.

9. Are you involved in any clubs or activities at school?

A. You bet. You're busy organizing the school disco at the moment and all the hippest people are going to be there.

B. You tend to concentrate on your lessons, but your friends sometimes drag you along to after-school activities.

C. You live for writing workshops and the drama society, unless they clash with your art club, of course.

10. What is your attitude to what you wear?

A. It should be versatile and practical, as you never know what you might be doing.

B. Your clothes reflect your desire to express yourself, so you tend to mix-and-match, and create something unique.

C. Something simple and comfortable that you feel yourself in. You're not out to impress anyone.

Now turn to page 88 and work out your score.

Know Your Inner Self

Everyone knows that being yourself is the way to go, but did you know that there are aspects of your personality which may not be obvious even to you? Investigate your dreams and reveal how you are really feeling, and take our career quiz to uncover your dream job. Take a deep breath, and prepare to sink deep into your subconscious.

Dream On

In the quest to discover the true you it is vital that you enter the mysterious and fascinating world of dreams. Did you know that your dreaming mind has access to information that is not readily available to you when you are awake? Dreams can reveal your innermost desires and feelings. On pages 47 to 49 is a list of some of the most common subjects of dreams and their meanings. When you read the interpretations, think about how they relate to your own experiences and to what is going on in your life.

Dream Fact File

Over a third of your life will be spent sleeping.

In your lifetime, you will spend approximately six years dreaming.

You dream, on average, for one or two hours every night, and often have between four and seven dreams.

Five minutes after the end of the dream, 50% of the content is forgotten. After ten minutes, 90% is lost.

If you are snoring, then you cannot be dreaming.

Animals: Dreaming of a dog means that people close to you are loyal. If the dog is happy, you are at peace with yourself or in love. If the dog is angry, you are worried about being betrayed. A sheep means you are following the crowd and not thinking for yourself. A cat means you have good instincts and should learn to trust your feelings.

Aeroplane: You are coping well with any problems that come your way.

Birds: A goose can be a sign that you have acted unwisely. An ostrich indicates you have been ignoring unpleasant facts. A nightingale means you are longing for something.

Car: In your dreams, a car symbolizes your physical body. So ask: is it working properly? Are you behind the wheel or is someone else in control? Are you driving it safely? What is the road like — rocky, winding, or does it suddenly end at the edge of a cliff?

Chased: You are avoiding something you don't think you can handle. If you are doing the chasing then you are trying to achieve something difficult.

Clouds: Clear blue skies mean the future looks bright; dark clouds mean trouble is brewing.

Crush: It's not unusual to dream about the boy you fancy; if you dream about a boy but you can't see his face or you don't know who he is, it means you are looking for a relationship.

Death: This means the end of something that keeps happening, or a habit that you are trying to break; it can also mean that you are feeling angry with someone.

Door: Representing the entrance to a better place, this means that new opportunities are coming your way. Locked or closed doors may represent an obstacle or opportunities that are not currently available to you.

Drinking: This is a good sign and it means you have a thirst for achievement, or perhaps just something simple, like a new CD.

Flying: Flying signifies freedom. This could mean either that you have a desire to escape something, or that you are perfectly content with your surroundings and are feeling the freedom of being yourself.

Getting Lost: You are worried about the future.

Home: This represents security. You are feeling safe and confident. An attic symbolizes development and progress. A hallway symbolizes a journey that needs to be completed. A bathroom symbolizes a need for cleansing. A kitchen reflects supplying the body and mind. If the food is plentiful, you have what you need. If the cupboard is bare, this indicates a need for something new to fulfil you.

Key: You have a problem to solve, but you also have the ability to work it out.

Money: Dreaming of being rich means you are feeling confident; dreaming of being poor means you are feeling unsure of yourself.

Teeth: Dreaming that your teeth fall out means you are finding it hard getting your voice heard or your feelings acknowledged.

Water: Rivers and streams mean you are journeying from one stage of life to another, or you might be watching other people travel down the river while you are stuck where you are; lakes and ponds are calming and they mean you are feeling happy; thunderstorms represent washing away the old to make room for the new.

What Is Your Dream Job?

Have you ever thought about what career path you might follow once school's out forever? Whatever you think you might want to be — singer, journalist, doctor, mechanic — do this quiz and discover your dream job.

Read the statements over the next few pages and circle the symbols alongside those that appeal. Add up which symbol appears the most and then check out your job type. Happy job hunting!

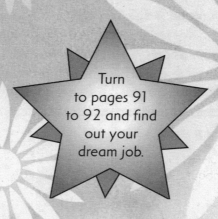

Turn to pages 91 to 92 and find out your dream job.

My friends always come to me for advice and I love to give it.	★
I often scribble down ideas for songs or poems.	●
My favourite lessons are maths or science.	■
If there's a big issue to be debated then I'm your girl!	★
I spend a lot of time just thinking about things.	●

When I get my own car I will try to find out how it works.	■
I'm the life and soul of the party.	★
I'd rather be outside in the fresh air than sitting in a classroom.	●
I enjoy working with my hands.	■
I'm always first to audition for the school play.	●

In a big group, I like to sit back and see what other people have to say.	●
I love taking things apart to see how they work and then putting them back together again.	■
I'm very good at getting others to see things from my point of view.	★
I often sit and think up new ways of tackling things.	■
Eating out with friends is great, but it's a good job I'm on hand to sort out the bill.	■

If I worked in an office I would want to have a lot of say in how things were done.	★
I'm writing a play/short story at the moment.	●
If I accidentally break something then I try really hard to fix it.	■
I don't care what I end up doing as long as I'm helping others.	★
I'm really good at making a story about me sound more exciting than it actually was.	●

I like to follow instructions so I get an important job done properly.	■
I'd quite like to work for a charity when I get older.	★
If I'm signing a card or buying a present for someone I spend a lot of time over it and try to make it personal.	★
My bedroom is really neat and tidy – even my CDs are in alphabetical order.	■
Most of my mates know who I fancy.	●

I miss essay deadlines more often than not – I've often got other thoughts on my mind.	⬤
When I'm surfing the Internet I head straight for the chat rooms.	★
I am interested in why my friends and family think and feel the way they do.	★
I have designed the set for a school play.	⬤
I enjoy learning facts.	■

What Is Your Boy Karma?

Bet you flicked to this section of the book first! Here's the part where you get to ask vital questions about the inhabitants of Planet Boy.

Got a best boy bud who you think wants to be more than just friends? Maybe the stars can help you out if you're deciding whether you and the boy you've got your eye on are destined for a date. If thoughts of love are on your mind, this is the section to study.

Written In The Stars

Want to know if the stars say you and your crush are destined for love? Whether you're crazy for the boy next door, or you want to know how you match up with that pop god (just in case you ever happen to bump into him), try this astrological chart to see how your star signs work together.

Check Your Star Sign

What sign are you? What sign is your crush? You'll have to find out his birthday first (no stalking him, though).

Aries: March 21st – April 19th
Taurus: April 20th – May 20th
Gemini: May 21st – June 20th
Cancer: June 21st – July 22nd
Leo: July 23rd – August 22nd
Virgo: August 23rd – September 22nd
Libra: September 23rd – October 22nd
Scorpio: October 23rd – November 21st
Sagittarius: November 22nd – December 21st
Capricorn: December 22nd – January 19th
Aquarius: January 20th – February 18th
Pisces: February 19th – March 20th

Using The Star Chart

Find your star sign on the top row of the grid on pages 60 and 61. Follow the column down until you find the star sign belonging to your crush. In the box where the two columns meet you'll see a code. Use the key below to find out what the code means.

Key

GL: Good Luck – It doesn't seem like you're a very good match. Maybe he'd make a good friend. Besides, his mate is really cute.

UAD: Up And Down – While you make brilliant mates, becoming anything more could be a bad move and it'd be a shame to spoil a great friendship.

PWF: Playing With Fire – This relationship looks like it could be fiery. You might have to compromise quite a lot to make it work, so think before you rush in to it.

MTM: More Than Mates – This match is a good one. You have lots in common and would enjoy hanging out together. There wouldn't be many arguments either.

MTB: Meant To Be – Wow, you've found a perfect lurve match. You could have some really cool times with this person. You should be great together.

star sign	Aries	Taurus	Gemini	Cancer	Leo
Aries	PWF	UAD	MTM	GL	MTB
Taurus	UAD	MTB	GL	MTB	PWF
Gemini	PWF	GL	MTB	GL	UAD
Cancer	GL	MTM	UAD	MTB	GL
Leo	MTB	PWF	PWF	GL	PWF
Virgo	GL	MTB	UAD	MTM	GL
Libra	UAD	UAD	MTB	UAD	MTM
Scorpio	UAD	PWF	GL	MTB	PWF
Sagittarius	MTB	MTM	MTM	GL	MTB
Capricorn	MTM	MTB	GL	MTB	MTM
Aquarius	MTM	GL	MTB	GL	MTM
Pisces	GL	MTB	GL	MTB	UAD

Virgo	Libra	Scorpio	Sagittarius	Capricorn	Aquarius	Pisces
GL	UAD	PWF	MTB	GL	MTM	UAD
MTB	UAD	PWF	MTM	MTB	GL	MTM
MTM	MTB	UAD	MTM	GL	MTB	GL
MTM	GL	MTB	GL	PWF	GL	MTB
GL	MTB	MTM	MTB	GL	UAD	MTM
MTM	GL	MTM	GL	MTB	UAD	MTB
GL	MTM	GL	MTB	MTM	MTB	MTM
PWF	UAD	MTB	UAD	MTM	GL	MTB
GL	MTB	UAD	PWF	GL	MTM	MTM
MTB	MTM	PWF	GL	MTB	GL	MTB
UAD	MTB	UAD	MTM	GL	GL	MTM
UAD	GL	MTB	MTM	MTM	MTM	MTB

Is He A Mate
Or A Date?

Boy buds are great for giving you a different point of view. They're top at all sorts of advice on life, love or that new skirt that you're thinking of buying. Who better to go to for an honest opinion than your closest male mate, especially when it comes to your latest crush?

Sometimes though, friendships with boys can get a bit tricky if you start to develop feelings for them. And what if they fancy you back? How can you tell?

By carefully observing his behaviour around you, you might discover if you are destined to be dates, or just mates. Read each of the statements in the chart on page 63 and, if it applies to you and your boy bud, put a tick in the box.

If you tick more than four boxes, the next time you see him could be for your first date.

BEHAVIOUR	TICK
He's always giving you hugs.	
He often stands close enough to you that your arms touch.	
He always listens to what you're saying, even if you're just talking about the weather.	
He gives you compliments all the time.	
He goes silent when you talk about boys you fancy.	
He thinks you look great even when you're wearing your oldest clothes and you haven't washed your hair.	
He makes excuses to spend as much time with you as possible.	
When you have a favour to ask he's first in line to help.	
He has favourite songs that remind him of you.	
You keep catching his eye.	
He calls and texts you every day.	
He cancels plans with his mates to be with you.	

Love Wordsearch

Can you find the words of love hidden below? Good luck!

valentine	romance	destiny
cutie	dating	boyfriend
lush	crush	kiss

C	R	N	V	N	V	T	Y	D
D	G	O	L	K	A	U	N	E
N	E	E	G	I	L	R	T	S
E	S	C	N	S	E	N	C	T
I	E	N	Y	S	N	G	R	I
R	I	A	R	B	T	N	U	N
F	T	M	A	N	I	I	S	Y
Y	U	O	I	W	N	T	H	C
O	C	R	G	O	E	A	U	M
B	R	L	U	S	H	D	P	A

Know Your Friends

You might be surprised to find a section about your friends inside a book that's supposed to be helping you find the true you. However, who your friends are, and how you relate to them, are all crucial in understanding more about your own personality. The gossip game on pages 66 and 67 is the ultimate game of truth — so be prepared to be totally honest and to hear things about yourself that you might not expect. Follow the instructions carefully, and get ready to dish the dirt.

The Gossip Game

How to play

Before your friends arrive at your house, cut out pages 68, 70 and 72 along the dotted line and cut out each statement. Fold the pieces of papers up and put them all in a hat.

Decide which friend is going to start. Say, for example, you decide your mate A is to be the first Gossip Guru. Everyone except mate A picks out a statement. Then, your mate B (on A's left) begins the game by reading out the statement and filling in the gossip. For example:

> 'In an argument, A will always —
> ...repeat her point of view endlessly.'

if this is B's opinion of A's argument skills!

Moving in a clockwise direction, the next person picks out a statement and adds their gossip, and so play continues.

When everyone in the circle has revealed their gossip (depending on the size of the group, you can go around as many times as you like), Mate A must try to remember everyone's statement about herself in order to survive and continue playing. If she forgets one, she is out. The person on her left becomes the next Gossip Guru, and play is repeated until the last player remains, who becomes the true Gossip Guru.

Get gossiping!

CUT HERE

If the Gossip Guru could choose a funky holiday it would be...

The Gossip Guru always wears clothes that are...

If the Gossip Guru's got to meet her crush, she would...

The Gossip Guru's most cringe-worthy moment was...

The Gossip Guru's fave subject at school is...

There's a rumour going around about the Gossip Guru which is...

The Gossip Guru thinks the best teacher at school is...

GOSSIP GURU GAME

GOSSIP GURU GAME

GOSSIP GURU GAME

GOSSIP GURU GAME

GOSSIP GURU GAME

GOSSIP GURU GAME

GOSSIP GURU GAME

To chill out the Gossip Guru likes to...

The Gossip Guru spends all her money on...

If a friend went to the Gossip Guru needing some words of wisdom she would...

The Gossip Guru's idea of keeping fit is to...

If there is someone the Gossip Guru really doesn't like it's gotta be...

If the Gossip Guru could go to see one band or pop star in concert it would be...

If the Gossip Guru could be a famous actress, she would be...

GOSSIP GURU GAME

GOSSIP GURU GAME

GOSSIP GURU GAME

GOSSIP GURU GAME

GOSSIP GURU GAME

GOSSIP GURU GAME

GOSSIP GURU GAME

The Gossip Guru's most annoying habit is…

The Gossip Guru thinks the best colour in the world is…

If she was having a bad hair day the Gossip Guru would…

If the Gossip Guru was chilling out in front of her favourite film it would be…

In an argument the Gossip Guru will always…

If the Gossip Guru was pigging out on her favourite food it'd have to be…

The Gossip Guru doesn't know that…
fancies her

GOSSIP GURU GAME

GOSSIP GURU GAME

GOSSIP GURU GAME

GOSSIP GURU GAME

GOSSIP GURU GAME

GOSSIP GURU GAME

GOSSIP GURU GAME

Quiz Seven

Do You Really Listen?

Would you be surprised to know that hearing and listening are not the same thing? Listening involves engaging with your friends, and is an active process in which you really take on board what is bothering them, rather than just nodding in the right places. Complete this quiz and find out whether your counselling skills are super or shameful.

1. My friends come to me for advice.

A. Most of the time
B. Sometimes
C. Almost never

2. I would describe myself as a good listener.

A. Most of the time
B. Sometimes
C. Almost never

73

3. When two of my best friends have a major fight I decide who is right and take sides..

A. Most of the time
B. Sometimes —
C. Almost never

4. Even when a friend's opinion differs wildly from my own, I take the time to see her point of view...

A. Most of the time —
B. Sometimes
C. Almost never

5. If a friend rings me with a problem while my favourite television programme is on, I'll turn the TV off and talk to her there and then.

A. Most of the time —
B. Sometimes
C. Almost never

6. If a friend told me a really big secret, I tend to find it really hard not to blab.

A. Most of the time
B. Sometimes
C. Almost never —

7. If a friend keeps coming back to me with the same problem, but never follows my advice, I get annoyed with her.

A. Most of the time
B. Sometimes
C. Almost never —

8. I would help solve a good friend's problem even if it could get me into trouble.

A. Most of the time —
B. Sometimes
C. Almost never

9. Because I think I give excellent advice, I tend to offer an opinion on other people's problems even if they don't ask for one.

    A. Most of the time
     B. Sometimes —
    C. Almost never

10. When someone comes to me with a dilemma I take it as a chance to leap in and tell a similar story of my own.

    A. Most of the time
     B. Sometimes —
    C. Almost never

The Answers

In this section you will find out what all your answers say about you. So go ahead, discover the true you.

Answers To Quiz One:

How Assertive Are You?

1. A=10, B=5, C=0
2. A=0, B=10, C=5
3. A=10, B=5, C=0
4. A=0, B=5, C=10
5. A=5, B=0, C=10
6. A=10, B=0, C=5
7. A=5, B=10, C=0
8. A=10, B=0, C=5
9. A=0, B=10, C=5
10. A=10, B=0, C=5

80-100 Points, Overkill?

Wow, the word bossy doesn't do you justice! You are extremely dominant and people just can't refuse you, mainly because they can't get a word in edgeways. People enjoy being in your company because of the excitement you radiate, but they may hesitate to become too deeply involved with you. Beware: if you constantly walk all over family and friends, they may start walking away from you. Sit back a little and let someone else have a go. Life in the background could be quite relaxing for a bit, and it'll give other people the chance to shine like you.

60-79 Points, The Perfect Balance

Cool, you know exactly when to speak and when to keep quiet. You're good at standing up for what is important to you and dealing with difficult situations. Others see you as someone who is the centre of attention, but balanced enough not to let it go to your head. Friends know they can come to you for good advice as you are someone who will cheer them up and help them out. Nice one, girl!

Under 60 Points, You Are Important Too!

Oh dear, it looks like you could do with speaking up for yourself a bit more. People may think you are shy, nervous and indecisive, whereas you may simply be being cautious, careful and practical. It's fine to let others get what they want, but don't let them treat you like you don't exist. What you need is important too and true friends will realize this. Think about letting your voice be heard a bit more. You don't have to be pushy, but with a little more confidence you could find yourself really going places.

Answers To Quiz Two:

Keen On Green?

1. A=0, B=10, C=5
2. A=5, B=0, C=10
3. A=10, B=5, C=0
4. A=0, B=10, C=5
5. A=10, B=0, C=5
6. A=5, B=10, C=0
7. A=0, B=5, C=10
8. A=10, B=0, C=5
9. A=5, B=0, C=10
10. A=10, B=5, C=0

80-100 Points,
Green Machine

Wow! Protecting the planet is definitely a top priority for you, and you're not afraid to stand up for what you believe in. Friends and family are used to you telling them to get recycling or to start eating organic. There's not a lot you don't know about environmental issues or the things that can be done to make a difference. Go girl — the Earth is safe in your hands.

60-79 Points,
Part-time Planeteer

You know quite a lot when it comes to things green, and you're happy to do your bit. While you're not occupying the nearest endangered woodland in a bid to protect it, if everyone took your lead we'd live on a much healthier planet. Keep up the good work, but perhaps have a think about what more you could do.

Under 60 Points,
Eco-challenged

If someone asked you to find your local recycling centre you'd probably just stare blankly at them. You don't really care about the difference between leaded and unleaded petrol, but it's not too late to change the way you treat the planet. Start off by making sure you turn lights off when you leave a room, and think before you drop litter on the ground. You'll soon find being green comes naturally. Good luck!

Answers To
Quiz Three:

Are You Open-Minded?

1. A=10, B=0, C=5
2. A=0, B=10, C=5
3. A=5, B=10, C=0
4. A=10, B=5, C=0
5. A=5, B=0, C=10
6. A=10, B=5, C=0
7. A=10, B=5, C=0
8. A=10, B=0, C=5
9. A=5, B=0, C=10
10. A=0, B=5, C=10

80-100 Points:
Prejudiced Personality

'Stick with what you know' is your motto. You have a circle of really close mates so feel that you don't need anyone else. Watch out. You'll never get to know new people if you judge them before giving them a chance. If someone suggests doing something different, don't run a mile. Open your mind a little and prepare to be pleasantly surprised.

60-79 Points:
Suspicious Sister

You can't make up your mind whether to give something a chance or play it safe. You're curious about new people and situations, so be a bit more adventurous. When that little voice tells you to stick your head in the sand, ignore it and follow your heart.

Under 60 Points:
Broad-minded Babe

If it's different then you're up for it. You always give new people and experiences a chance. You don't judge people on how they look or what you've heard about them. But take care. It's still cool to say no when you think a situation could be dangerous – it doesn't mean you're being narrow-minded, just careful.

Answers To Quiz Four:

What Is Your Fashion Type?

Classic

You are the one that all your friends come to for fashion advice, the one that everyone wants to go shopping with! You aren't always swayed by the latest fashions, but you always look good and pulled together. You like clothes that make you feel comfortable and presentable the whole time. You tend to go for classic, neutral colours, but are equally as happy in jeans and T-shirts.

Cutie

You always like to look pretty, sweet and very feminine. Your fashion expertise isn't just restricted to clothes — you also have an obsession with make-up, jewellery, face and hair products. You tend to prefer soft colours — it is guaranteed that you own more than one pink item. You are comfortable in skirts, dresses and heels, and know how to perfect the beautiful girly look.

Original

Your look is always new, fresh and cool. You like to dress in your own way. You don't follow a defined style, but have a talent for combining different items to create a unique overall look. You probably have a penchant for visiting charity shops or raiding your mum's old clothes, and you enjoy customizing outfits. Having such stylish instincts your friends can rely on you to tell them whether their own outfits look good or bad.

Glamour Puss

You are definitely a real fashion diva. Your style is a little bit rebellious, crazy and different, but most of all it is completely up to date with what is being sported on the catwalks. You aren't ashamed of spending hours getting ready because you love every minute of it. Bright and bold shoes and dark mysterious colours are ideal for you. Keeping up with ever-changing fashion styles is not easy, but it's definitely worth every penny.

Answers To Quiz Five:

What Is Your Personal Style?

1. A=1, B=2, C=3
2. A=3, B=2, C=1
3. A=2, B=3, C=1
4. A=2, B=3, C=1
5. A=3, B=1, C=2
6. A=1, B=2, C=3
7. A=3, B=1, C=2
8. A=1, B=2, C=3
9. A=2, B=3, C=1
10. A=2, B=1, C=3

22-30 Points:
Sorted Sister

You are really down-to-earth and love the simple things in life. You believe that family and friends are what it's all about and without them you'd be lost. Mind you, where would they be without you? You're a rock to your loved ones. You are the person everyone comes to for advice and a hug. Steady and secure, you know what you like and you're not out to impress anyone. You are one sorted sister.

13-21 Points:
Go Girl, Go

Life for you is one big rollercoaster ride of people, parties and pleasure. It seems like you're always into something new, and the more people who join in the merrier. You have a wide circle of friends, and with your 'go getting' attitude you're guaranteed to remain the life and soul of the party. Just make sure you don't burn yourself out — learn how to relax.

1-12 Points: Creative Character

You've always got something on your mind. You spend a lot of time trying to understand different people and situations. You're very creative and you are proud of being different. Left on your own, you're perfectly content. You're an open-minded individual who has always got something smart to say. Make sure you keep in touch with your mates and get out there and do things, not just think about them.

Answers To Quiz Six:

What Is Your Dream Job?

People

You seem to be really good at working with people. You are a natural leader, and perhaps enjoy making speeches and debating. You are interested in people and what makes them tick, and would be well-suited to a job where you train or advise people. Workmates will love you for your ability to motivate, and you will find fulfilment in being able to help people.

Possible careers:
Politician, Teacher, Social worker, Charity worker, Police officer, Firefighter, Doctor, Nurse

Creative

You love anything creative, whether that involves working artistically, musically, or with the written word. However, working eight hours a day in an office may not satisfy your burning desire for self-expression. You are an original thinker with a great imagination, and therefore a career where you are called upon to develop and create your ideas will be of particular interest to you.

Possible careers:
Artist, Actor, Writer, Chef, Musician, Designer, Journalist, Producer, Broadcaster.

Logical / Mechanical

You have a particular skill, and interest, in the practical – numbers, machines and how things work. You like order and being organized. Logical through and through, you carry out tasks thoroughly, and detail is important to you. You may have an aptitude for science, mathematics or economics, and enjoy the rigorous and exact nature of those subjects.

Possible careers:
Manager, Lawyer, Banker, Biologist, Physicist, Engineer, Economist, Entrepreneur, Computer programmer.

Answers To Quiz Seven:

Do You Really Listen?

1. A=3, B=2, C=1
2. A=3, B=2, C=1
3. A=1, B=2, C=3
4. A=3, B=2, C=1
5. A=3, B=2, C=1
6. A=1, B=2, C=3
7. A=1, B=2, C=3
8. A=3, B=2, C=1
9. A=1, B=2, C=3
10. A=1, B=2, C=3

21-30 Points:
Dilemma Diva

You give such excellent advice it's a wonder you don't have your own website! Your mates appreciate your clear-headed, sensitive approach to their problems. You don't seem to have any problem listening and giving time to your friends, and you are no doubt appreciated for it. Your non-judgmental approach means that you can assess situations from many different perspectives. Well done — you are a valued and respected friend. Let's hope everyone listens to your words of wisdom.

11-20 Points:
Hit And Miss

You love your mates to bits, but sometimes you just can't find the energy to listen to another of their problems. When you do, your advice is invariably flawless, but sometimes it's just that bit too much effort. That's fair enough if you're always the person they come to, but try to be sympathetic. They choose you for a reason, and you'll want them to be there for you when you're in a muddle.

Under 10 points:
Fairweather Friend

Hmmm...you may be far too wrapped up in yourself to be interested in anybody else. You tend to act as if there is only one person worth thinking about — and that's you. You might think that you do give advice when it's needed, but think about it — does it usually involve telling a story about yourself? Beware, eventually people will start looking elsewhere for advice and friendship.

Under The Magnifying Glass

Now that you know who you are,
stick a picture of yourself in the square
below and be proud of the true you.